writing guides

ACTIVITIES FOR
Instructions

JILLIAN POWELL

CONTENTS

INTRODUCTION

The Scholastic *Writing Guides* series provides teachers with ideas and projects that promote a range of writing, bringing insights from educational research into the classroom. Each guide explores a different type of writing and provides example material, background information, photocopiable activities and teaching suggestions. Their aim is to enable teachers to guide the writing process, share planning ideas and develop themes as a context for writing activities.

The materials:
● motivate children with interesting activities
● break complex types of writing into manageable teaching units
● focus on and develop the typical features of particular types of writing
● provide original approaches to teaching.

Each book is divided into sections, beginning with examples of the type of writing being taught. These are followed by ideas for developing writing and projects that will extend over a series of sessions.

Section One looks at good examples of the genre, with the emphasis on using texts to stimulate and develop writing. Two example texts are shared, and questions that focus the discussion on their significant features are suggested. This is followed by activities that explore what the texts can teach us about writing, enabling teachers to compare the two texts and to go on to model the type of writing presented in the guide.

Section Two moves from reading to writing. This section provides activities that prompt and support children in planning and writing. A range of approaches includes planning templates and strategies to stimulate ideas. The activities refine children's ideas about the type of writing being developed and give them focused writing practice in the context of scaffolded tasks. Teacher's notes support each activity by explaining the objective and giving guidance on delivery.

Section Three moves on to writing projects. Building upon the earlier work in Section Two, these projects aim to develop the quality of writing and provide a selection of ideas for class or group work on a particular theme or idea. The teacher may choose to use some or all of the ideas presented in each project as a way of weaving the strategies developed in Section Two into a more complex and extended writing task.

Section Four supports the assessment process. Children are encouraged to reflect on the type of writing they are tackling and to evaluate how effectively their work has met the criteria for the genre identified in Section One.

Recipe for a knickerbocker glory

You will need

I punnet of strawberries	sundae glass
I punnet of raspberries	knife
I peach	sieve
tub of vanilla ice cream	jug
chocolate sprinkles	bowl
small pot of whipping cream	whisk
glacé cherry	tablespoon

Follow these instructions on how to make a really yummy knickerbocker glory.

● First, whisk the cream in the bowl until it is fluffy.

● Now press the raspberries through the sieve into the jug. You can do this using the back of the spoon. This makes the raspberry sauce.

● Cut the skin off the peach then slice it into small pieces.
● Next, put some strawberries into the sundae glass.
● Scoop in some of the ice cream.
● Add the peach pieces on top.
● Now pour over the raspberry sauce.
● Spoon some of the cream on top.
● Sprinkle some chocolate on top.

● Finally, top with the glacé cherry.

● Find a clean spoon and enjoy!

writing guides: **INSTRUCTIONS**

How to clean your rabbit's hutch

Do this every day:

1. First, remove any droppings with a plastic scoop.
2. Next, throw away old food from your rabbit's dish.
3. Wash the dish well and dry it with a cloth.
4. Finally, make sure your rabbit has plenty of clean water and fresh hay.

Do this once or twice every week:

1. First, use a dustpan and brush to sweep out the hutch.
2. Throw away the old hay, wood shavings and paper.
3. Now dip the brush into some warm soapy water and scrub the inside of the hutch. Rinse with clean water.
4. Let the hutch dry, then spray it with disinfectant.
5. Lay clean paper over the bottom of the hutch and cover it with clean wood shavings and hay.
6. Scrub the inside of the rabbit's water bottle using soapy water and a bottlebrush. Rinse it out well with lots of fresh water until all the soap has gone.
7. Wash your hands well when you have finished.

A dirty hutch can breed germs, so to keep your rabbit in good health, remember to clean out its hutch regularly.

writing guides: **INSTRUCTIONS**

Although children may be unfamiliar with the term instruction texts, *they will be familiar with instructions in everyday life, for example the instructions for playing a board game or a computer game, or the instructions for children's craft activities or recipes. Instruction texts explain processes clearly, using devices such as short, clear sentences, bulleted lists and diagrams. They convince the reader that he or she can successfully undertake a task or procedure, by making it sound straightforward and achievable, and using friendly, reassuring language. Writing instructions will help children organise material in a clear, chronological order; write sentences that are clear and concise; and address their readers with appropriate language.*

Shared activities

Recipe for a knickerbocker glory

This recipe for making a knickerbocker glory or an ice cream sundae illustrates many of the generic features of writing instructions: a title which explains what the recipe is for, a list of ingredients and equipment needed, a series of instructions set out in a clear, chronological order, and diagrams. It is written in short, concise sentences and the tone is friendly and encouraging, so that the reader is tempted to try out the recipe.

Read through the recipe with the children. Ask them if they know what a recipe is (instructions for making a food dish). Do they think they could make their own knickerbocker glory? Point out how the recipe starts by listing all the ingredients and equipment needed. Remind them that it is important that the instructions are set out in the right order, as the knickerbocker glory is built up in a tall sundae glass, starting with the bottom layer. Ask them to identify all the linking words that help one step in the instructions follow on from another (such as *first, now, next*). Which words might encourage them to try the instructions? (*Yummy, enjoy.*) What helps make the instructions clear and easy? (Short sentences and diagrams.)

How to clean your rabbit's hutch

These instructions demonstrate how a procedure can be taught in a series of numbered steps, written in concise sentences. The style is more formal than the recipe, with the emphasis on clarity. There is an imperative verb towards the start of each instruction (*let, scrub, remove* and so on), so the children will become familiar with the sentence pattern for the instructions as they read through. Read the text with the children and ask them where they think these instructions might appear – for example, in a vet's surgery waiting room, or in a pet-care book. Ask them why they think it would be important for a pet owner to follow these instructions. (It wouldn't be very nice for the rabbit living in a dirty hutch, and also the rabbit could pick up germs and become ill.) Ask the children to identify some of the items they would need in order to follow the instructions, for example a plastic scoop, a bucket of warm soapy water. Can they think of any other similar instructions that might appear in a pet-care manual, for example how to bathe a dog, groom a cat and so on? They could try to find some other examples at a vet's surgery or in the library.

Seven steps

Display 'Recipe for a knickerbocker glory' from photocopiable page 4. Look at the words which have been picked out on photocopiable page 8 and remind the children that they are all verbs – doing words. Tell them that these particular verbs are imperative verbs – this is the type of verb they will be using when they are writing instructions to tell someone how to do something. A good example of an imperative verb is the instruction *Sit!* or *Stay* when training a dog. Ask the children if they can think of other imperative verbs that might be used in another recipe. Write their suggestions on the board (for example, *stir, mash, mix, chop* and so on.) Go back to the knickerbocker glory recipe and point out how each step in the instructions follows the same pattern, with the imperative verb towards the start of the sentence. Repeating this sentence pattern helps keep the instructions clear while the linking words (*first, next* and so on) emphasise the right order.

Now ask the children to look at the recipe and work out how to complete each sentence on photocopiable page 8. Work through the sentences with the class, then ask them to cut them out and work in pairs to rearrange them in the right order. When they are happy with the order, they can paste them in place on a fresh sheet. They can also add some linking words, using the suggestions on the sheet.

Rabbit, rabbit!

Display the instructions on photocopiable page 5 alongside a copy of the chart on photocopiable page 9. Look at the chart together and tell the children that they are going to be listing all the items or equipment needed to clean a rabbit hutch. Just as recipes begin with a list of ingredients, 'how to' instructions should begin with a list of all the things you need to do the task. Read through the instructions with the children and ask them to stop each time they hear an item of equipment. Write each item they find on the board or flip chart, then work together through photocopiable page 9, listing each item separately in the left-hand column, and explaining what it is used for in the right-hand column.

Taking ideas further

Easy does it

The activity on photocopiable page 10 invites the children to compare the two samples of instructions. The questions highlight genre features shared by the two texts. They ask the children to consider where these instructions might appear, and how they use devices such as lists to make the procedure easy to follow and encourage confidence in the reader. They also invite children to think about how diagrams or illustrations can support the texts.

Just the recipe!

Photocopiable page 11 uses the form of a recipe to draw together key features of instructions that the children have come across so far, as well as suggesting other techniques or devices that they will be using in Section Two activities. It can be enlarged as a classroom poster and used for reference when the children are discussing or writing instructions.

Extension ideas

● Encourage the children to become more familiar with the instructions genre by collecting other examples. These could include information sheets such as the Green Cross Code or other safety instructions, pet-care leaflets, DIY leaflets, the rubrics for games or sports, and 'how to' craft instructions such as those sometimes found on the back of cereal packets.

● Collect examples of single sentences taken from instructions and spend a shared session asking children to suggest the context or guess the activity. (For example, *cut around the dotted line* – making a paper mask or model; *stir well* – making a cake or pudding; *find your lifejacket under your seat* – safety instructions on an aeroplane.)

Seven steps

Here are seven steps to make a knickerbocker glory.
Complete each sentence then cut them out and rearrange
them in the correct order. Paste them in place, then number
the steps or add some linking words, for example:

First   Then   Next   Finally

Slice _____

Sprinkle _____

Pour _____

Press _____

Spoon _____

Add _____

Whisk _____

Rabbit, rabbit!

In the left column, list all the equipment and materials that you need to clean out a rabbit hutch. In the right column, write down what each item is used for.

What do you need?	How is it used?
plastic scoop	to clean out rabbit droppings

Easy does it

Instructions	Recipe for a knickerbocker glory	How to clean your rabbit's hutch
Where might these instructions appear?		
Write an example of how the writer uses a list.		
Write an example of a linking word.		
Which words or phrases make the task sound fun or worth doing?		
Are there any pictures or diagrams?		

Just the recipe!

How to write instructions

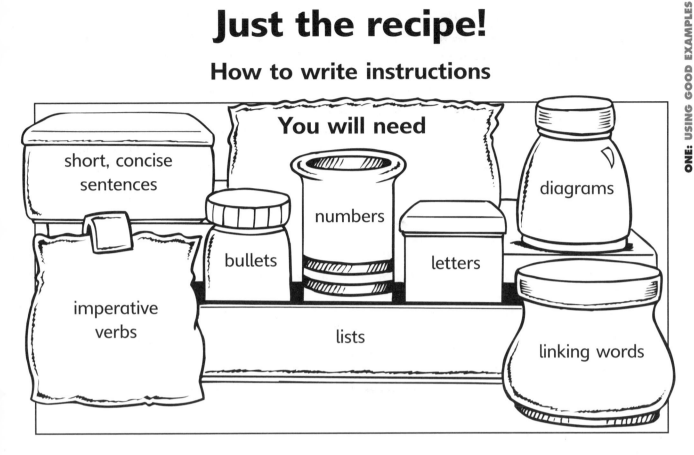

You will need

short, concise sentences

imperative verbs

bullets

numbers

letters

lists

diagrams

linking words

1. State your goal in the title.
2. List all equipment and materials needed.
3. Write in a clear sequence.
4. Use short, concise sentences.
5. Keep the tone friendly and encouraging.
6. Use diagrams where they will help explain the text.
7. End with an encouraging statement.

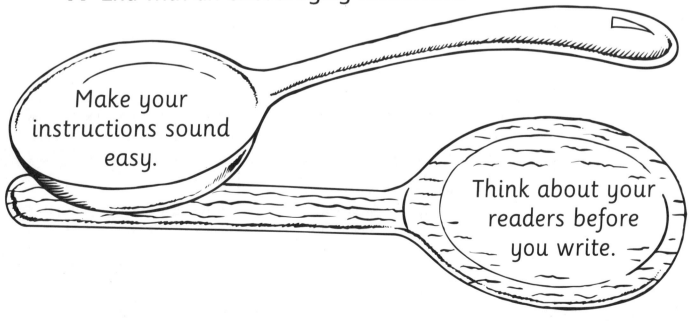

Make your instructions sound easy.

Think about your readers before you write.

SECTION TWO

DEVELOPING WRITING

The activities in this section are designed to help children understand the generic features of instructions. Each activity focuses on a different aspect of writing instructions, such as the use of imperative verbs or bulleted lists, writing a sequence of steps in chronological order, and using diagrams to clarify text. The activities also introduce different types of instructions, such as rules or guidelines and 'how to' craft or games instructions. They involve some class work and discussion as well as individual or pair work to complete the sheets. They will generate ideas for writing instructions and develop skills that can be used in Section Three to plan and write complete sets of instructions.

OBJECTIVE

■ To plan and list the items needed to complete a task or activity.

TAKE ONE
WHAT YOU NEED
Photocopiable page 15, writing materials, board or flip chart.

WHAT TO DO
Remind the children of the instructions for making a knickerbocker glory in Section One. The instructions began by listing all the things that were needed to make it. Tell the children that when they are writing instructions for how to make or do something, they should start by making a list of everything needed for that task. If they are writing a recipe, their instructions will need to list all the ingredients and equipment needed. For a craft activity, like painting or model-making, it will be all the materials and tools needed, such as paper and paintbrushes.

Hand out copies of the photocopiable sheet and explain to the children that they should think about the things needed for each activity or task on the sheet. (For younger or less able children, you may want to cover the bottom one or two boxes before photocopying.) When they have completed the sheets, they can work in pairs and compare their suggestions.

For an extension activity, the class could work in pairs or groups, with one side thinking up an activity and the other side working out all the ingredients and equipment that it would require.

OBJECTIVES

■ To break down a task into a sequence of simple steps.
■ To use numbers or bullet points to put material in order.

ONE, TWO, THREE
WHAT YOU NEED
Photocopiable page 16, writing materials, board or flip chart.

WHAT TO DO
Tell the children that instructions often involve several steps or stages, and it is important to set them out in a clear order. Explain that it can help to set out the steps as a list using numbers, letters or bullet points. It may be useful to show an example of bullet points on the board, for example to instal software on a computer:
● Turn on the computer.
● Load the CD.
● Click on the instal button.

Hand out copies of the photocopiable sheet and explain to the children that they are going to think about how to do a number of simple tasks. They need to break each one down into three steps that describe how to do the task, and in what order. They should keep their sentences as short and clear as possible so each one can be listed as a clear bullet point. When they have finished, ask them to work in pairs or groups to compare their suggestions and see which instructions are clearest.

writing guides: **INSTRUCTIONS**

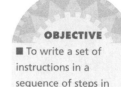

ONE STEP AT A TIME

WHAT YOU NEED

Photocopiable page 17, writing materials.

WHAT TO DO

Remind the children that the instructions they looked at in Section One had a clear order – that is, they explained to the reader that he or she must first do this, then do that. The instructions followed a clear sequence, step by step. Hand out the photocopiable sheet and explain to the children that the picture strip illustrates instructions for making home-made lemonade. Tell them that they need to look at each picture and write a sentence below it giving the instructions for that step. Before they start filling in the sheet, remind the children that it may be helpful to think of words such as *first*, *now* and *next* to link up their sequence of instructions. For example, *First, cut the lemons in half* or *Now add six cups of water*. When they have finished filling in the sheet, they can then use the pictures to help them write a list of all the ingredients and equipment needed to make lemonade on the back of the sheet.

When the children have completed the activity, they can work in pairs to compare their instructions to see which work best.

OBJECTIVE
■ To write a set of instructions in a sequence of steps in chronological order.

HOW TO PLANT A BULB

WHAT YOU NEED

Photocopiable page 18 (two copies per child), paper, scissors, glue, writing materials.

WHAT TO DO

Hand out copies of the photocopiable sheet and explain to the children that this is a set of instructions for planting a flower bulb, but that all the steps have been muddled up. Each child will need two copies of the sheet. They need to read them through carefully and work out the right order for planting the bulb. They should use one sheet to cut out all the sentences then juggle them around until they are happy that they are in the right order. They can then use the other sheet and paste the sentences back in the right order. Finally, they should fill in the 'What you need' box by writing down five items that are needed for the task. When they have completed both tasks, work as a class to check through their results and make sure all steps are in the right order and that they have listed the appropriate equipment.

For an extension activity, the children could try illustrating each step with a simple diagram.

OBJECTIVES
■ To plan and list materials needed for a task.
■ To set out the steps of a procedure in order.

JUST DO IT!

WHAT YOU NEED

Photocopiable page 19, writing materials, board or flip chart.

WHAT TO DO

Tell the children that they see instructions all around them every day. Good examples are signs like *Keep off the grass*, *Now wash your hands* and *Drive carefully*. Ask them to try and think of some more examples of instructions that they might see in public places like roads, parks, swimming pools or zoos, for example *Eat before fuelling* at a service station, or *Don't feed the animals* in the zoo. Write their suggestions on the board. The children should be encouraged to start collecting different examples of instructions. These could include traffic signs – either using words or signs – such

OBJECTIVE
■ To understand and practise the use of imperative verbs.

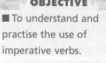

as 'No entry' signs, or signs giving orders such as *Pedestrians cross here*, or *Cross to the other pavement*.

Now ask the children if they can find the 'doing word' in one of the instructions you have written on the board – that is, the verb. Refer them back to the work they did for 'Seven steps', photocopiable page 8, in Section One. Remind them that a verb used to give an order or instruction is an imperative verb. Work through each of the instructions on the board with the class, circling all the imperative verbs.

Tell the children that they will need to use imperatives when they are writing instructions. They are going to think up some imperative verbs that they can use for a wall chart to go in a kitchen. Hand out the photocopiable sheets and ask the children to read the six cooking rules. Now ask them to write down an imperative verb which will fit each space. In some cases, more than one verb will fit. When they have finished, ask them to read out and compare some of their suggestions.

PICTURE IT
WHAT YOU NEED
Photocopiable page 20, coloured and black crayons or felt-tipped pens.

OBJECTIVE
■ To use simple diagrams to illustrate the stages of a process.

WHAT TO DO
Tell the children that when they are writing 'how to' instructions, it may sometimes help if they draw simple diagrams to show what they mean. Hand out photocopiable page 20. Explain that this is a leaflet giving instructions to circus clowns on make-up. Read the leaflet with the children, pointing out key generic features, such as the list of 'What you need', and the use of numbered points and imperative verbs.

The children will need to choose a number of coloured crayons or felt-tipped pens to illustrate each stage of the instructions. They should first read each instruction carefully and then draw and colour the clown faces to illustrate each step, using a black felt-tipped pen or crayon for any outlines. (Remind them that they will need to repeat the previous steps at each stage of the colouring, to show the clown's face at each stage of the painting.)

GET SET, PLAY!
WHAT YOU NEED
Photocopiable page 21, writing materials.

OBJECTIVE
■ To write key sentences for instructions to simple games.

WHAT TO DO
Remind the children that all kinds of games – computer games, ball games, board games, party games – need instructions. These provide information, such as how many players can take part, what you need to play the game, how the game starts, what happens next, and how you win the game. Hand out copies of the photocopiable sheet and explain to the children that they are going to think about a simple game that they are familiar with. They can choose from the suggestions on the sheet or think up one of their own. They should then fill in the spaces by answering the questions. For example, *How many people can play?* might be answered with *Two people can play this game* or *This game can be played by two or more people*. When they have finished, they can work in pairs and try guessing from the answers what kind of game their writing partner is describing.

Take one

Instructions often begin with a list of ingredients or equipment needed. Write down three things that you would need for each of these activities.

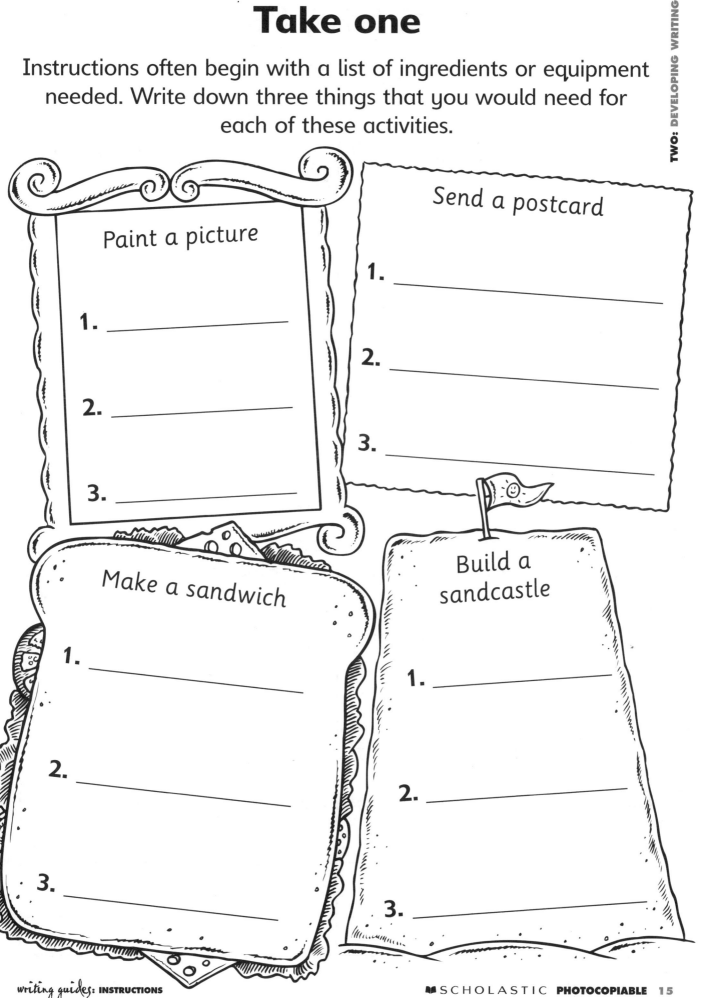

Paint a picture

1. _____

2. _____

3. _____

Send a postcard

1. _____

2. _____

3. _____

Make a sandwich

1. _____

2. _____

3. _____

Build a sandcastle

1. _____

2. _____

3. _____

One, two, three

Think about each activity and then write instructions for how to do it in three steps.

Blow up a balloon

1. _____

_____

2. _____

_____

3. _____

_____

Clean your teeth

1. _____

_____

2. _____

_____

3. _____

_____

Paint a potato print

1. _____

_____

2. _____

_____

3. _____

_____

Play hide-and-seek

1. _____

_____

2. _____

_____

3. _____

_____

One step at a time

Here are some pictures showing how to make home-made lemonade. Write a sentence in each box giving step by step instructions.

How to plant a bulb

These instructions are in the wrong order. Cut them out and paste them onto another sheet in the correct order. Finish by filling in the 'What you need' box.

What you need

1. _____   4. _____

2. _____   5. _____

3. _____

Cover the pot and leave in a cool dark place for about six weeks.

Water well.

Fill the pot half full with compost.

Put a few pebbles in the bottom of the pot.

Cover with more compost just leaving the top of the bulb showing.

Sit the bulb on the compost.

Just do it!

Here are six cooking rules. Each one has an imperative verb missing. Find a verb to fit each space.

1. [   ] your hands before you begin.

2. [   ] your hair back if you have long hair.

3. [   ] the recipe carefully.

4. [   ] ingredients before you begin.

5. [   ] oven gloves to pick up hot pans.

6. [   ] chopping boards clean.

Picture it

Diagrams can help explain your instructions. Colour the clown faces to show each stage of painting a clown's face. Complete the instructions by filling in the 'What you need' box.

How to paint a clown face

What you need
_____   _____
_____   _____

1.

Paint a white base all over the face.

2.

Paint a big red smile around the mouth.

3.

Paint purple squares around the eyes.

4.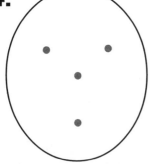

Paint a black line around the red and purple areas.

5.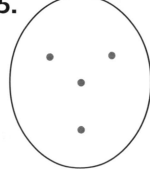

Paint two black eyebrows.

6.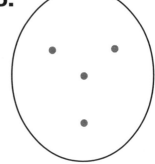

Paint the nose red.

Get set, play!

All kinds of games – computer games, board games, ball games and party games – need instructions. Choose a game and fill in the table.

Here are some games you could choose:

musical chairs

hide-and-seek

your favourite computer game

rounders

Name of game	
How many people can play?	
What do you need to play?	
How does the game start?	
What happens next?	
Who wins?	
Why is it fun?	

SECTION THREE
WRITING

This section helps the children to develop complete instruction texts using the ideas they have explored in Sections One and Two. The activities support the children through developing and writing different forms of instructions.

Reference is made to the tasks completed in Sections One and Two, and the children will be able to make use of ideas and vocabulary generated by those tasks. It will be helpful for children to have access to the photocopiable pages they completed for Section Two and to the sample texts and 'Just the recipe!' poster from Section One.

Throughout this section, encourage children to write their ideas in full sentences and paragraphs where necessary, using clear concise sentences and a friendly, encouraging tone.

Come to my party

The activity on photocopiable page 23 helps children give clear instructions for geographical directions, using a simple map. The children look at a map that shows the location of an imaginary school and a home where the party is being held. Explain that they need to write directions to their friends to tell them how to get to the house. They can send out these instructions with the party invites. They should write down the directions step by step, referring to all the local landmarks (church, shops, letter box and so on) to help their guests get from the school to the house. They can then fold the page, write their invitation on the front page, and decorate it with pictures of balloons, birthday cakes and so on.

Instruct an alien

The illustrations on photocopiable pages 24–5 encourage children to think about familiar everyday activities and write instructions explaining how to do them in terms that even an alien could understand. Explain that they are writing instructions for an alien who has landed on planet Earth and wants to learn how earthlings live and copy them. They should write down instructions for each activity on a separate piece of paper, keeping the language as simple as possible. Remind them that they can keep their instructions clear by using short concise sentences and setting out each step in order, using a list with numbers, bullet points or letters.

Obstacle race

This activity encourages children to write instructions for taking part in an obstacle race on the school sports day, using picture and word prompts provided on photocopiable pages 26–7. They should write the instruction for each activity shown on the sheet (including starting and finishing).

Stay safe at the seaside

The activity on photocopiable pages 28–9 asks children to write some instructions for a safety leaflet about staying safe at the seaside. Explain that the picture shows some hidden dangers at the seaside, and the children are going to write instructions for avoiding them and staying safe. Look at the picture and labels with the children and work through the dangers, asking them if they understand what might happen – for example, someone could cut their foot on a broken bottle. Choose one example, such as swimming when the red flag is flying, and ask the children what they would write to warn people against it. Write one of their suggestions on the board, for example *Do not swim in the sea when the red flag is flying*. The children can then work on their own or in pairs to complete the sheets using the picture prompts to help them.

Come to a party

Imagine a party is being held at a house after school on Friday. Write simple instructions telling your friends how to get to the party from school. Then fold and decorate your invitation.

How to get to the house

fold

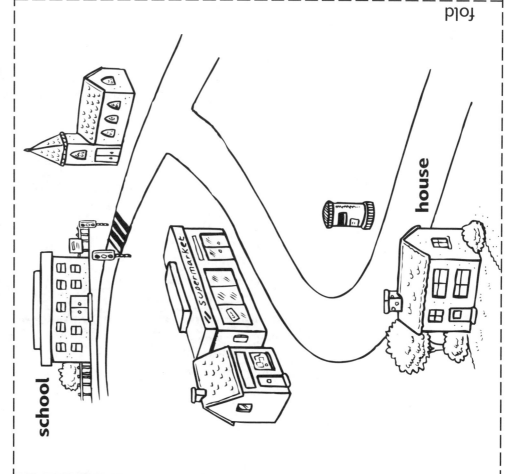

school

house

Supermarket

Instruct an alien

Write simple instructions for an alien on how to behave like an earthling.

writing guides: **INSTRUCTIONS**

DRESS LIKE AN EARTHLING

HAVE AN EARTHLING PARTY

Obstacle race

Write some instructions for an obstacle race for the school sports day.

First _____

_____

Then _____

_____

Next _____

_____

Then _____

_____

You can use these verbs to help you.

run   crawl   skip   climb   jump

Now _____

_____

Then _____

_____

Next _____

_____

Finally _____

_____

Stay safe at the seaside

This picture shows some hidden dangers at the seaside.

Write some instructions to help families to stay safe.

writing guides: **INSTRUCTIONS**

Inflatables can be blown out to sea.

It's dangerous to climb and dig in cliffs.

SECTION FOUR
REVIEW

This section helps the children to identify strong and weak points when they are writing instructions, and to evaluate other examples of the genre. It provides you with an opportunity to review how well the children have understood and are using key features of the genre.

In assessing instructions, it is helpful to suggest any areas where the instructions might be confusing or difficult to follow, or where they do not give enough information.

As they review their work, remind the children of the generic features of instructions (detailed on photocopiable page 11) and encourage them to refer back to the activities they completed for Sections Two and Three. Children can undertake the reviewing activities individually, working with a writing partner, or in groups.

Children's self-review

Check it out

The children can use this chart to review instructions they have written, or those written by their classmates. They should check through their work to see if they can find good examples of key features of the genre. If a feature is missing, or seems weak, they can try to improve their text by suggesting additional sentences or by revising what they have written.

Is that clear?

Photocopiable page 32 provides children with a framework to criticise and improve an instructions text. They are given an example of a weak instructions text on how to grow a pineapple plant. Prompts are provided to help them identify flaws in the text and make improvements. They can also use these prompts as guidelines when reviewing their own work or that of a writing partner.

Other review methods

● Ask the children to work in pairs with a writing partner who assesses how easy their instructions are to follow, raising questions if any points are confusing or not clear.
● Encourage the children to collect examples of 'visual' instructions (pictograms), such as the green/red man at traffic lights, traffic signs, warning symbols.
These could form part of a classroom display, with children interpreting the signs in words, for example *A green flashing man means 'cross the road now'.*
● For discussion, think about all the places where instructions are needed: for example, model kits, public places such as swimming baths and sports halls, and board or computer games.
● Look at some leaflets on subjects such as safe cycling or safety in the home. Discuss with the children how clear the instructions are, and if there is anything that could be added or made clearer.

Suggested resources

● Copies of leaflets and pamphlets giving instructions, especially those aimed at children, for example copies of the Green Cross Code.
● The rubric and instructions for children's board and computer games.
● Recipe books aimed at children/young cooks.
● 'How to' craft and activity books for children.
● The Highway Code, and other books of signs and symbols.

writing guides: **INSTRUCTIONS**

Check it out

Can you find examples of these key features in your instructions text?

Feature	Example
Title explaining goal of text	
List of ingredients/ materials needed	
Numbers, letters or bullet points	
Short, concise sentences	
Linking words, eg then, next	
Friendly, encouraging tone	
Diagrams or illustrations	
Rounding-off sentence	

Is that clear?

These instructions for growing a pineapple plant
need more work!

Can you think of a helpful title?

Break the task down into
several steps and use numbers
or bullets.

You can grow a pineapple
plant from a bit of a
pineapple. Let it dry out first.
Get a pot with some pebbles
and sand and compost in. Put
the pineapple on and add
some more compost round it.
Water it and cover the pot
with a plastic bag and leave
it on a warm windowsill. Don't
take the bag off until the new
leaves start growing. Water
the new plant well.

How long?
(2 days)

Which bit?
(the top)

How
much?
(half each)

How long?
(2 weeks)

Start by listing what you
need.

Can you make
the activity
sound more fun
or interesting?

Can you think of a sentence to
round off the text?

writing guides: **INSTRUCTIONS**